TABLE OF CONTENTS

Story Clues

clown

pen

giggle

wiggle

I got a new pen.

The pen is red with a
clown on the end.

When I write, the clown wiggles
and my sister giggles.

What Did the Story Say?

 Write the words to answer the questions.

pen   sister   clown

What is the birthday gift?_____

Who wiggles?_____

Who giggles?_____

Word Families __own

 Write the words.

fr + own   frown

d + own   _____

br + own   _____

cl + own   _____

 Draw a line to the matching picture.

frown   down   brown   clown

Story Clues

fish

read

home

school

This is Jim. Jim is a fish.

Jim goes to school.
It is a fish school.

Jim learned to read. He likes to read at school and at home.

What Did the Story Say?

ABC Write the answers.

What is Jim? _____

What did Jim learn to do? _____

Where does Jim like to read?

_____ and _____

Jim the Reading Fish

Catch the Match!

 Color two pictures in each row that rhyme.

Story Clues

birds

seeds

cold

winter

feeder

Birds have a hard time finding food when it's cold. They need our help.

We put the seeds in the feeder
and fill it up — but not too much!
Then we put the feeder in the yard.

We like to feed the birds in the winter.
They like when we feed them, too.

What Did the Story Say?

 Color the pictures of things from the story.

BIRD FEED

Weather Words All Around

 Draw an X on the weather words.

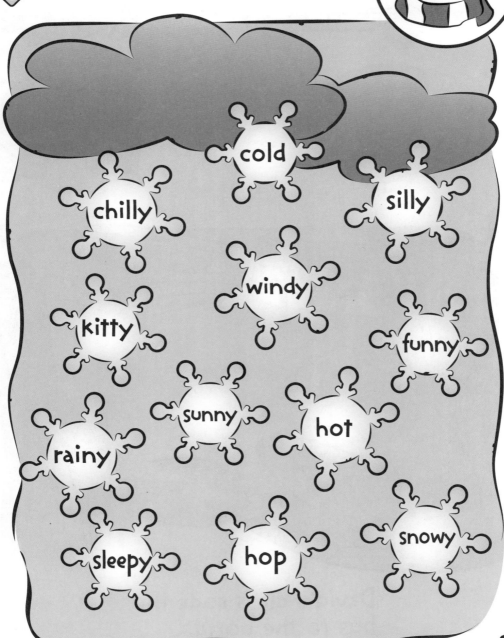

cold

chilly

silly

windy

kitty

funny

sunny

hot

rainy

sleepy

hop

snowy

13

Story Clues

bus

pond

net

turtle

David's class rode the
bus to the pond.

The pond was green and slimy.
The class was surprised to see ducks,
frogs, fish, and some water bugs.

A snapping turtle in David's net was the biggest surprise!

What Did the Story Say?

 Draw a line to the answer of each question.

Where did the class go?   ducks, frogs, fish,
                                           and water bugs

What color was the pond?
                                                    green

What did the class see
at the pond?   pond

What was the surprise in   bus
David's net?

                                                  snapping
                                                   turtle
How did the class get to the pond?

The Pond

  Color the things that belong at the pond.

Story Clues

basket

kitten

blanket

pocket

bucket

puppet

The kittens sleep in a basket with a soft blanket. Their toys are in the bucket for playtime.

A pocket makes a fun toy for a busy kitten. A puppet can be a toy, too.

Playing makes the kittens sleepy again.

What Did the Story Say?

 Write and draw the answers.

Where are the kitty toys?

What do the kittens find to play with?

Where do the kittens sleep?

Word Endings
-et or -en

 Write the correct ending for each word.

chick _____   pupp _____

blank _____   kitt _____

 Write a word from above to finish each sentence.

My _____ keeps me warm.

The _____ lays eggs.

Watch the _____ dance on strings.

"Meow," says the _____ .

The Jungle Room

Story Clues

door

plant

chair

row

food

table

There is a room in Grandma's house at the end of the hall. Open the door and what do you see?

There are plants on the table, plants on the chair, plants on the floor — plants everywhere!

We call it the jungle room. We row our boats down the jungle river until it's lunchtime.

23

Then we eat jungle food in our hut.

What Did the Story Say?

Mark an X in the box next to the correct answer.

Where does the story take place?
- ☐ at school
- ☐ outside
- ☐ at Grandma's house

Where is the room full of plants?
- ☐ in the bathroom
- ☐ at the end of the hall
- ☐ in the basement

What do the children call the room with plants?
- ☐ the jungle room
- ☐ the play room
- ☐ the bedroom

Where do the children eat lunch?
- ☐ on the river
- ☐ in their boats
- ☐ in their hut

Look What's Growing!

 Write the type of each plant using the word list.

_____

_____

_____

_____

_____

_____

_____

| bush | cactus | flower | fruit |
| grass | tree | vegetable | |

Story Clues

hairy

yellow

spotted

wave

striped

There are so many things to see at the zoo.

The tall, spotted giraffes eat from the top of the tree.

The striped zebras run on the hills.

The bright, yellow parrot talks to the others.

The big, hairy gorilla eats a banana.
I wave and smile . . . and the little
gorilla waves back.

What Did the Story Say?

 Write the word to finish the sentence.

The _____ has stripes.

The _____ is hairy.

The _____ has spots.

The yellow _____ talks.

The _____ waves back.

Silly Gorilla

  Draw and color the rest of the gorilla.

Story Clues

baby

raccoon

bat

tent

bear

wolf

We were all sleeping snug in our tent.

A strange sound woke us up.

It was scratching.
It was licking.
It was sniffing.
It was kicking.

Could it be a bear?
Could it be a wolf?
Could it be a raccoon?
Could it be a bat?

Oh, what strange sounds a hungry baby can make at night.

What Did the Story Say?

Write four strange sounds that the family heard.

1. _____   3. _____

2. _____   4. _____

Circle the word that tells why the baby made strange sounds.

The baby was:

scared	happy	hungry	sleepy

Animal Sounds

 Draw a line from the animal to the sound it makes.

bark

quack

oink

roar

meow

moo

Story Clues

city

moon

cloud

planet

country

star

Looking up at night you can see many bright lights. It's fun to look at the stars.

But the city lights can make the stars hard to see. Clouds can make them even harder to see.

35

The stars are much easier to see in a country sky. And on a clear night you can see even more — like the Earth's moon and other planets.

What Did the Story Say?

Write and draw the answers.

What is fun to see at night?

_____

What are two things that make stars harder to see?

_____and _____

What else can you see in the sky on a clear night?

_____

Word Families_ ight

 Write the word.

l + ight _____   t + ight _____

n + ight _____   r + ight _____

Same Sounds

 Circle the words that sound like light.

knight

kite   bright

sit   flight   lit   height

bite   late   white   hit

feet   quite

quiet

37

Story Clues

climb

shellfish

float

rock

fur

water

The sea otter has such warm fur.
It can stay in the water all day long.

A sea otter finds tools underwater to help it eat. It can use a rock to crack open a shellfish.

The sea otter likes to float on its back in the water. It also likes to climb on the rocky beaches.

What Did the Story Say?

 Complete the sentences to show four things you learned about the sea otter.

1. The sea otter has warm _____.

2. The sea otter can use a rock to crack

   open a _____ for food.

3. The sea otter likes to float on its

   _____ in the water.

4. Sea otters like to climb on _____

In Otter Words

 Write the answers to complete the puzzle. If you need help, use the word list.

Across

2. What is shell + fish?
5. Where does the otter find tools to help it eat?

Down

1. How long can an otter stay in water?
3. What is a name for animal hair?
4. Where does the otter live?

sea   all day   shellfish
fur   underwater

Story Clues

bowl

pot

carrot

salt and pepper

lollipop

stove

Jane and Jan wanted to help Mom make supper. They took out a large pot to make a fancy soup.

salt and pepper

lollipops

sugar

orange juice

carrots

First, they put in orange juice.
Next, they put in carrots and lollipops.
Then, they added salt and pepper and some sugar.
Last, they stirred and stirred until the soup was well mixed.

43

Jane and Jan's soup cooked on the stove for a long time.

When it was ready, Jane and Jan made sure Mom was the first to try their fancy soup. Mom did not feel fancy at all. She felt sick.

What Did the Story Say?

Circle the things that Jane and Jan put into the soup.

Your Yucky Food Story

 Write about something you ate that did not taste good.

_____

_____

_____

A Fancy Soup for Mom

Just Add Chocolate

 Write the numbers to put the pictures in the right order.

47

Story Clues

cat

frog

butterfly

puddle

duck

robin

finish line

FINISH

worm

START

Cat, Frog, Robin, and Duck came to win the race. Goat said, "Go!" and the race began.

Down the street they went
as fast as they could.

Cat ran very fast.
Frog hopped very fast.
Robin flew very fast.
Duck waddled slowly.

49

Cat saw a butterfly and chased after it.
Frog saw a puddle and jumped in for a swim.
Robin saw a worm and stopped
for a snack.
Duck was tired but raced on.

While the others were too busy to race, Duck crossed the finish line.

Good job, Duck! You won the race!

What Did the Story Say?

 Circle the sentences that are true.

The race started when Cow said, "Go!"

Cat, Frog, Robin, and Duck were all in the race.

Cat went off to chase a fly.

Frog jumped in a puddle to swim.

Robin found a worm to eat.

Duck was too tired to finish the race.

Goat ran fast.

Cat ran very fast.

Cat won the race.

Duck won the race.

Draw your own race with your favorite animals.

 Write who you think would win your race and why.

_____

_____

_____

_____

53

Story Clues

blanket

mittens

chair

scarf

hat

sweater

needles

yarn

Granny took out some big balls of yarn. She had many colors. There was pink, orange, green, blue, purple and white.

Granny sat in her rocking chair and started knitting. She knitted so fast her needles looked like lightning.

When the sun came up, Granny was finished. She knitted a whole closet full of winter things. There was a blue hat, green scarf, orange sweater, purple sweater, and pink mittens.

Granny wrapped the new things to give us as gifts. Then she wrapped herself in the new white blanket that she knitted and took a long nap.

What Did the Story Say?

 Circle the word that tells where the sentence belongs in the story.

Granny sat in her chair and knitted.

Beginning	Middle	End

Granny took out some big balls of yarn.

Beginning	Middle	End

Granny took a nap with her new white blanket.

Beginning	Middle	End

New Things to Wear

  Color the things Granny knitted and write their names below.

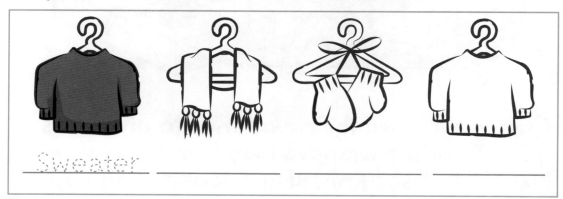

Sweater _____ _____ _____

Granny's Colorful Yarn

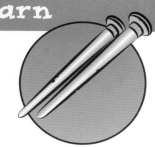

If I Could Knit

 Draw a picture of what you would knit if you could.

Write about what you drew.

I would make _____

because _____ .

Granny's Colorful Yarn

 Write the name of each color.
If you need help, use the word list.

60

Granny's Colorful Yarn

yellow   blue   purple   black   white
green   red   brown   orange   pink

Answer Key

My New Pen

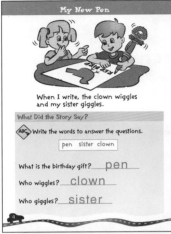

When I write, the clown wiggles and my sister giggles.

What Did the Story Say?

ABC Write the words to answer the questions.

pen   sister   clown

What is the birthday gift?   pen

Who wiggles?   clown

Who giggles?   sister

My New Pen

Word Families ___own

ABC Write the words.

fr + own   frown

d + own   down

br + own   brown

cl + own   clown

Draw a line to the matching picture.

frown   down   brown   clown

Jim the Reading Fish

Jim learned to read. He likes to read at school and at home.

What Did the Story Say?

ABC Write the answers.

What is Jim?   a fish

What did Jim learn to do?   read

Where does Jim like to read?

home   and   school

Jim the Reading Fish

Catch the Match!

Color two pictures in each row that rhyme.

Feeding Birds at Wintertime

We like to feed the birds in the winter. They like when we feed them, too.

What Did the Story Say?

Color the pictures of things from the story.

Feeding Birds at Wintertime

Weather Words All Around

Draw an X on the weather words.

cold   chilly   silly   windy   kitty   funny   rainy   sunny   hot   sleepy   hop   snowy

A Trip to the Pond

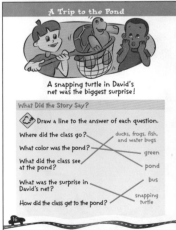

A snapping turtle in David's net was the biggest surprise!

What Did the Story Say?

Draw a line to the answer of each question.

Where did the class go?   ducks, frogs, fish, and water bugs

What color was the pond?   green

What did the class see at the pond?   pond

What was the surprise in David's net?   bus

How did the class get to the pond?   snapping turtle

A Trip to the Pond

The Pond

Color the things that belong at the pond.

Sleepy Kittens

Playing makes the kittens sleepy again.

What Did the Story Say?

ABC Write and draw the answers.

Where are the kitty toys?

in the bucket

What do the kittens find to play with?

puppet and pocket

Where do the kittens sleep?

basket

Answer Key

Sleepy Kittens

Word Endings
-et or -en

Write the correct ending for each word.

chick **en**   pupp **et**

blank **et**   kitt **en**

Write a word from above to finish each sentence.

My **blanket** keeps me warm.

The **chicken** lays eggs.

Watch the **puppet** dance on strings.

"Meow," says the **kitten** .

21

The Jungle Room

Then we eat jungle food in our hut.

What Did the Story Say?

Mark an X in the box next to the correct answer.

Where does the story take place?
☐ at school   ☒ at Grandma's house
☐ outside

Where is the room full of plants?
☐ in the bathroom   ☐ in the basement
☒ at the end of the hall

What do the children call the room with plants?
☒ the jungle room   ☐ the bedroom
☐ the play room

Where do the children eat lunch?
☐ on the river   ☒ in their hut
☐ in their boats

24

The Jungle Room

Look What's Growing!

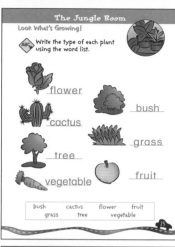

Write the type of each plant using the word list.

flower   **bush**

cactus   **grass**

tree   **fruit**

vegetable

bush	cactus	flower	fruit
grass	tree	vegetable	

25

What to See at the Zoo

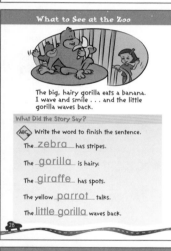

The big, hairy gorilla eats a banana. I wave and smile . . . and the little gorilla waves back.

What Did the Story Say?

Write the word to finish the sentence.

The **zebra** has stripes.

The **gorilla** is hairy.

The **giraffe** has spots.

The yellow **parrot** talks.

The **little gorilla** waves back.

28

What to See at the Zoo

Silly Gorilla

Draw and color the rest of the gorilla.

29

A Sound in the Night

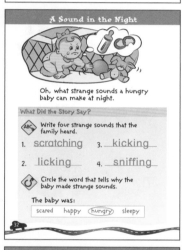

Oh, what strange sounds a hungry baby can make at night.

What Did the Story Say?

Write four strange sounds that the family heard.

1. **scratching**   3. **kicking**

2. **licking**   4. **sniffing**

Circle the word that tells why the baby made strange sounds.

The baby was:

| scared | happy | (hungry) | sleepy |

32

A Sound in the Night

Animal Sounds

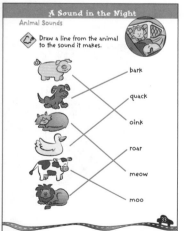

Draw a line from the animal to the sound it makes.

bark

quack

oink

roar

meow

moo

33

The Sky at Night

The stars are much easier to see in a country sky. And on a clear night you can see even more — like the Earth's moon and other planets.

What Did the Story Say?

Write and draw the answers.

What is fun to see at night?
stars

What are two things that make stars harder to see?
clouds and **city lights**

What else can you see in the sky on a clear night?
the Earth's moon and planets

36

The Sky at Night

Word Families _ight

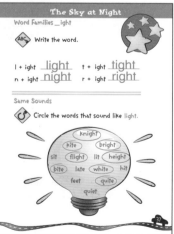

Write the word.

l + ight **light**   t + ight **tight**
n + ight **night**   r + ight **right**

Same Sounds

Circle the words that sound like light.

knight   bright
kite   flight   lit   height
sit   bite   late   white   hit
feet   quite
quiet

37

63

Answer Key

All About the Otter

The sea otter likes to float on its back in the water. It also likes to climb on the rocky beaches.

What Did the Story Say?

ABC Complete the sentences to show four things you learned about the sea otter.

1. The sea otter has warm **fur**.
2. The sea otter can use a rock to crack open a **shellfish** for food.
3. The sea otter likes to float on its **back** in the water.
4. Sea otters like to climb on **rocky beaches**.

40

All About the Otter

In Otter Words

ABC Write the answers to complete the puzzle. If you need help, use the word list.

```
    a
  s h e l l f i s h
    l   u
    l   e
  u n d e r w a t e r
    d
    a
    y
```

Across

2. What is shell + fish?
5. Where does the otter find tools to help it eat?

Down

1. How long can an otter stay in water?
3. What is a name for animal hair?
4. Where does the otter live?

| sea | all day | shellfish |
| fur | underwater | |

41

A Fancy Soup for Mom

What Did the Story Say?

Circle the things that Jane and Jan put into the soup.

Your Yucky Food Story

ABC Write about something you ate that did not taste good.

(Answers will vary.)

46

A Fancy Soup for Mom

Just Add Chocolate

ABC Write the numbers to put the pictures in the right order.

1 3
4 2

47

Race to the Finish Line

What Did the Story Say?

Circle the sentences that are true.

The race started when Cow said, "Go!"

~~Cat, Frog, Robin, and Duck were all in the race.~~ ✓

Cat went off to chase a fly.

~~Frog jumped in a puddle to swim.~~ ✓

~~Robin found a worm to eat.~~ ✓

Duck was too tired to finish the race.

Goat ran fast.

~~Cat ran very fast.~~ ✓

Cat won the race.

~~Duck won the race.~~ ✓

52

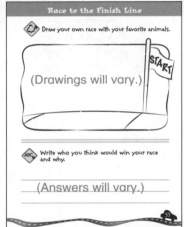

Race to the Finish Line

Draw your own race with your favorite animals.

(Drawings will vary.)

ABC Write who you think would win your race and why.

(Answers will vary.)

53

Granny's Colorful Yarn

What Did the Story Say?

Circle the word that tells where the sentence belongs in the story.

Granny sat in her chair and knitted.
Beginning (Middle) End

Granny took out some big balls of yarn.
(Beginning) Middle End

Granny took a nap with her new white blanket.
Beginning Middle (End)

New Things to Wear

ABC Color the things Granny knitted and write their names below.

sweater scarf mittins sweater

58

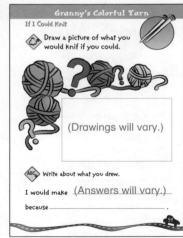

Granny's Colorful Yarn

If I Could Knit

Draw a picture of what you would knif if you could.

(Drawings will vary.)

ABC Write about what you drew.

I would make **(Answers will vary.)**

because _____

59

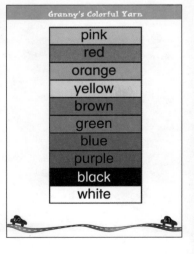

Granny's Colorful Yarn

| pink |
| red |
| orange |
| yellow |
| brown |
| green |
| blue |
| purple |
| black |
| white |

60
